FOLENS SPELLING

BASIC RULES

BOOK 1

Age 5–7

Glendra Read

CONTENTS

© 1993 Folens Limited, on behalf of the author.

First published 1993 by Folens Limited, Dunstable and Dublin.

Illustrations by Chris Masters.   Cover by Graphic Editions.

ISBN 185276389-2

Folens Limited. Apex Business Centre, Boscombe Road, Dunstable, LU5 4RL, England.

INTRODUCTION

This book and the National Curriculum

Spelling is seen as a 'Key Skill' in the Writing Attainment Target of the National Curriculum in English. The document stresses that spelling should always be seen and used in the wider context of literacy. Writing is a means of communication and children must be able to spell so that others can read what they have written. Spelling can be taught in a structured, developmental way, though as with every area of learning, children will learn at different rates and some will pick up spelling with ease, while others will experience great difficulty. This book aims to support teachers of children aged 5-7 years, working though National Curriculum Levels 1-3.

Level 1

Children should understand the basic differences between writing/drawing and letters/numbers, as well as being able to write down the basic letter shapes in response to sound. To reach this level, children should be able to write simple whole words using letters or groups of letters.

Level 2

Children should be able to produce a greater variety of commonly used, recognisable words. There is no stress however on the correct spelling of all words. This level emphasises the fact that single syllable words should be correctly spelt - those that follow simple patterns - and that knowledge of the alphabet should be evident by this stage. More patterns should be recognised and children should be seen to apply their knowledge of these patterns. This level is important as it is the one which should be reached by the 'average' 7 year old child.

Level 3

This goes beyond the previous two levels by stressing correct spelling of words of more than one syllable and highlighting new spelling terms such as 'vowels' and 'letter strings' and new language skills such as 'redrafting' and 'revising'. It is at this stage that accuracy is seen as being much more important in spelling.

This book offers a useful framework within which teachers can help children develop their skills for spelling well: understanding sound/symbol relationships, working through three and four letter words, mastering irregularly-spelt words, and discovering how words are derived and how they are put together and used. The range of sheets in this book offers varied activities for children of ages 5-7 years who may be at different stages, and acknowledges that children will learn as individuals although they will often be taught in groups. Sheets can be used accordingly.

This book is the first of three *Basic Rules* books. Book 2 is for 7-9 year olds, and book 3 is for 9-11 year olds.

What is in the book

There are 45 sheets in the book. As a rough guide, sheets 1-15 are aimed at the child working towards Level 1, pages 21-40 are for the child around Level 2, and pages 41-50 are for the more able 5-7 year old working towards Level 3. The book begins with basic sounds - beginning, middle and end sounds - and basic alphabet knowledge. There are sheets to practise regularly-spelt words (cat, hat, mat), and irregularly-spelt words (one, have, who). Some children will have difficulty with these latter words, and will need much practice to 'imprint' them. There are sheets to emphasise the importance of vowels, rhyme and syllables, and sheets to reinforce areas such as 'number', 'colours', and 'days of the week'. All the sheets have 'pointers' in the shape of animals, to show where the child needs to write or draw. There is a sheet to include parents in the learning process, and a self-concept sheet which may help children reflect on their performance as spellers and help them consider how to improve their spelling. At the end of the book are word lists, and an Appendix comprising a list of useful sources, including books, spelling programmes, workbooks and computer programs.

How the book can help with spelling

The book aims to:

1. Give children a multi-sensory strategy for learning a new spelling.
2. Suggest points for schools to look at when developing a whole-school spelling policy.
3. Give an overall progressive structure for the teaching of spelling.
4. Help children spell frequently-used words with confidence.
5. Help children 'generalise' from one known word to another word.
6. Support less able children, and extend more able pupils.
7. Give parents an opportunity to become involved in their children's learning.

Children need continuity and progression from early phonic knowledge and experimental beginnings towards conventional accuracy, so that they can use spelling meaningfully in the context of their own writing.

How to use the book

Sheets can be used for individual work, for work in pairs, or for group work. Sheets can be used as a follow-up to a class activity (e.g. alphabetical order, blends, or months), or given as homework to let parents help with spelling. Children who find spelling hard will need many reinforcement activities and much practice.

How to teach spelling

Teachers can help children develop the basic skills of spelling by encouraging them to speak clearly, listen carefully, look positively and write neatly. All the skills of speaking, listening, looking and writing combine in the complex and dynamic spelling process.

If children are given a spelling for a piece of work, all too often they **copy** it down. Copying is static and passive. It is vital to teach all children a method by which they may try to **learn** a spelling, so that when they transfer a word from the board or a dictionary to their own writing, they will begin to learn the spelling, not just copy without remembering. It may be useful to teach spelling in two stages.

In the earliest stages, children may find it easiest to try 'phonic spelling', where they listen for sounds and write down what they hear. This system directly relates the sound heard to the symbol written on the page. Children can listen for similar-sounding words, and begin to notice similarly-shaped words. Soon this reliance on phonics breaks down because of the idiosyncrasies of the English Language, and when children want to spell words like 'one' or 'who' the next stage is reached.

With a multi-sensory system (such as the one called 'simultaneous oral spelling', researched by Bryant and Bradley, see Appendix), children **look** at the word to be spelt; they **say** the alphabet letter names (which remain constant while sounds of letters vary) they **cover** the word and **write** it down. They then **check** what they have written. This method accords well with the National Curriculum advice to 'look, cover, remember, write, check'. The method includes looking, sub-vocalising, listening, writing and making a final visual check. Children can be helped by this method whether they have weak auditory memories or weak visual memories. Encouraging children to try out a spelling on a piece of paper can help them work towards the correct spelling of a word. Encourage them to 'have a go'.

Surely a spelling is either right or wrong?

In the early stages of learning, teachers need to help their pupils practise their emergent writing, and experiment with spelling inventions, so that they can feel like writers. The invention aspect helps children to think and learn as they move towards correct spelling. The role of the teacher is to correct work sensitively, and in the early stages it is important to give praise for the 'nearly-right' spelling. Looking carefully at errors in spelling can help identify **patterns** needing to be learnt, or irregular words to be practised, so that corrections can lead to new learning. Too many marks with a red pen will send obvious messages of rejection and failure to the writer, and may inhibit effort and make the writer afraid of writing.

How to move towards a whole school spelling policy

Developing a whole-school policy on spelling can be a useful activity, pooling teachers' ideas about spelling and the associated skills of handwriting and presentation. Each school needs to arrive at its own policy, taking account of the expertise of the teachers, the needs of the children, and recent research in the field.

Points to bear in mind

1. The need to respect children's efforts.
2. Teaching spelling from lists may not be the best way of helping children spell well in their own writing.
3. Children require grounding in basic word skills - alphabet knowledge, sound knowledge, the importance of vowels and the understanding of syllables.
4. All children benefit from spelling instruction.
5. Talking about spelling as a whole-staff activity brings out the wealth of knowledge and expertise that abounds, and ensures some sort of continuity and uniformity through the school.

Areas which could be discussed

1. A method to teach children how to learn a spelling.
2. 'Invented' spellings.
3. Basic word lists for year groups/subject-specific words (e.g. scientific words).
4. Marking policy (including error analysis).
5. Spelling tests.
6. Word books/dictionaries.
7. Handwriting and its association with spelling.
8. Rhyme.
9. Re-drafting/proof-reading.
10. Use of computers.
11. Diagnosis and remedy of spelling difficulties.
12. Games/materials/resources/books/schemes.

A series of staff meetings would be necessary before a final policy could be drawn up. Spelling policies should be dynamic, and be used, evaluated and adapted over time.

Spelling can be a daunting and frightening activity for children. By teaching children how to learn a spelling, by regarding errors with sympathy and understanding, and by encouraging thought and invention, we may help children to write purposefully and to convey their thoughts with confidence to the intended audience. Spelling is an integral part of the literacy scene, and needs to be taught meaningfully within the context of writing.

Beginning sounds 1

t   s   c   m   b

Write the beginning sounds.
Colour the pictures.

Now draw a new picture for each sound.

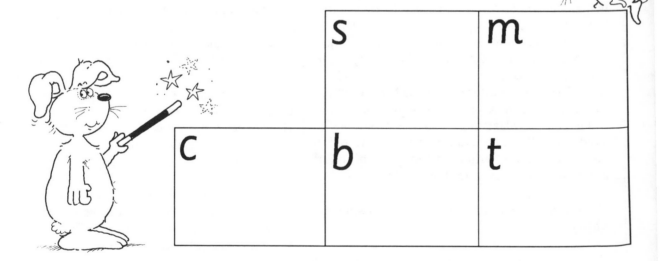

s	m
c	b	t

Say the sounds. Write them.

m m _____ _____ _____ _____
s s _____ _____ _____ _____
t t _____ _____ _____ _____
c c _____ _____ _____ _____
b b _____ _____ _____ _____

Beginning sounds 2

$f \quad d \quad k \quad g \quad p$

Write the beginning sounds.
Colour the pictures.

 f

 d

 k

g

p

Now draw a new picture for each sound.

g	k
d	f	p

Say the sounds. Write them.

d   d _____ _____ _____ _____

f   f _____ _____ _____ _____

k   k _____ _____ _____ _____

g   g _____ _____ _____ _____

p   p _____ _____ _____ _____

Beginning sounds 3

h   w   j   r   l

Write the beginning sounds.
Colour the pictures.

Now draw a new picture for each sound.

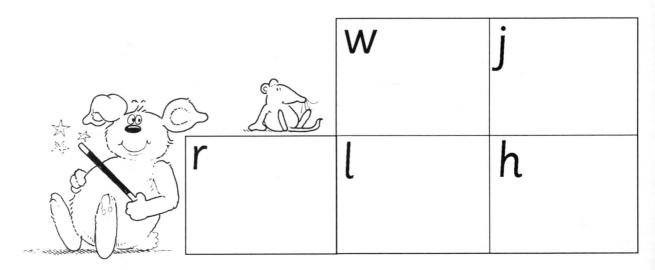

Say the sounds. Write them.

r
j
w   ____ ____ ____ ____
h
l

Beginning sounds 4

n   q   v   x   y   z

Write the beginning sounds.
Colour the pictures.

Now draw a new picture for each sound.

y	v	q
n	x	z

Say the sounds. Write them.

v   v _____   _____   _____   _____

y   y _____   _____   _____   _____

n   n _____   _____   _____   _____

q   q _____   _____   _____   _____

x   x _____   _____   _____   _____

z   z _____   _____   _____   _____

Vowels

a e i o u are vowels.
Join the vowel sound to the right picture.
Colour the pictures.

Say the sounds. Write them.

a a a _____ _____
e e e _____ _____
i i i _____ _____
o o o _____ _____
u u u _____ _____

Vowels in houses

a e i o u   are vowels

Put the words in the right houses.
Cross the words off as you go.
The first one is done for you.

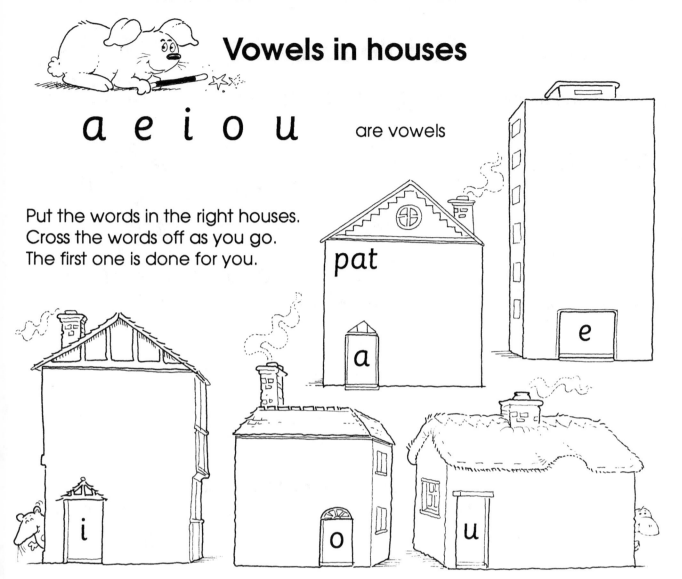

jug	cot	got	bed
	top	~~pat~~	cat
set	win	dog	bag
	bun	him	sun
sit	men	ham	gun
	pig	had	but
pet	Jim	red	not

Name _____   Date _____

Middle sounds 1

Put in the **middle** sound *a e i o u*

b_t   s_n   n_t

w_b   p_g   m_n

Write the words again. Read them.

_____   _____   _____

_____   _____   _____

Put a line under the **middle** sound.
Join with a line, words with the same **middle** sound.

sun   fat
hat   get
web   van
pig   bun
man   men
net   big

Write the letters across the page.

a _____

e _____

i _____

o _____

u _____

Middle sounds 2

a e i o u

Make new words by changing the **middle** sounds.
Draw a picture of your new word.
Write the word again.
The first one is done for you.

cut	⟶	c_a_t
dig	⟶	d_g
ten	⟶	t_n
big	⟶	b_g
rot	⟶	r_t
pat	⟶	p_t
sam	⟶	s_m

cat _____

_____

_____

_____

_____

_____

_____

Put in the **middle** sound.   a e i o u
Write the word again.

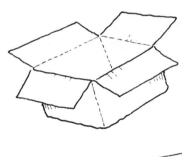

b_x

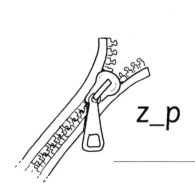

h_t

_____

g_n

_____

z_p

_____

p_n

_____

Name _____   Date _____

End sounds 1

Write the **end** sound to make the word.

k   g   t   s   p   n   d   m

ju_   foo_   be_   su_   zi_

bu_   han_   dru_   shi_

ti_   pra_   boo_   do_   ca_

Put a line under the **end** sounds.
Join with a line, words with the same **end** sounds.

jug	us
book	mat
cat	red
drum	hip
bed	rug
bus	run
ship	hum
sun	look

Read the words.

FOLENS SPELLING - Basic Rules Book 1 F3892   © Folens.

End sounds 2

Write the **end** sound to make a word.

Draw a picture for it. Write the new word.

su_   pi_   ca_

ha_   fo_   ru_

pe_   ma_   we_

Change the **end** sound to make a new word.
Write the new word.

bag ⟶ ba_ ⟶ _____

hum ⟶ hu_ ⟶ _____

peg ⟶ pe_ ⟶ _____

fog ⟶ fo_ ⟶ _____

cod ⟶ co_ ⟶ _____

sup ⟶ su_ ⟶ _____

lip ⟶ li_ ⟶ _____

cat ⟶ ca_ ⟶ _____

Read the new words.

Making words

Change the **beginning** sound to make new words.
The first one is done for you.

man	⟶	<u>c</u>an	⟶	fan
cat	⟶	_at	⟶	_at
hen	⟶	_en	⟶	_en
pig	⟶	_ig	⟶	_ig
top	⟶	_op	⟶	_op
sum	⟶	_um	⟶	_um

Read the new words

Choose a letter from box 1, a letter from box 2 and another letter from box 3 to make some 3 letter words.
Write the words on the lines underneath.
The first one is done for you.

Box 1	Box 2	Box 3
m g f	a e	<u>x</u> s
p t	i	p d
s d n		n t
b c	<u>o</u> u	m b g

fox _____

_____

_____

_____

FOLENS SPELLING - Basic Rules Book 1 F3892   © Folens.

Name _____   Date _____

Wordsearch 1

Learn to spell like this:

Look	Say	Cover	Write	Check

Spell these words:

is _____	of _____	and _____
in _____	a _____	the _____
I _____	to _____	was _____
it _____	he _____	that _____

Now find the words in the wordsearch.
All the words go across. ⟶
The first one is done for you.

h	e	b	i	n	g	a
i	c	t	h	e	i	t
w	a	s	p	t	o	m
i	s	r	a	n	d	u
t	h	a	t	v	o	f

Matching

Match up the 2 words which are the **same**.

cut	mop
red	red
dog	pig
pig	beg
nut	cut
dig	nut
can	dog
map	cat
beg	dig
mop	map
cat	can

Find the 2 words in the line which are the **same**.

(bad)	bed	(bad)	dab	bat	had
dog	god	dig	dod	dog	gob
pug	pud	bug	pug	pun	pup
can	cad	cat	con	can	nac
wed	web	ewb	wed	wep	wet
him	hin	mih	hem	hum	him
ten	ten	tin	net	tun	tan

Name _____   Date _____

Letters

Write your name _____

Now find and colour the letters for your name.

Name _____   Date _____

Rhyme time 1

Put 3 words in each balloon to **rhyme** with the word in the balloon.

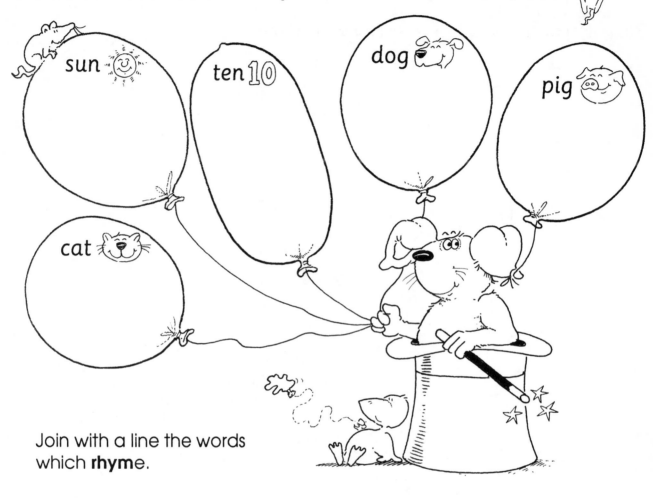

Join with a line the words which **rhym**e.

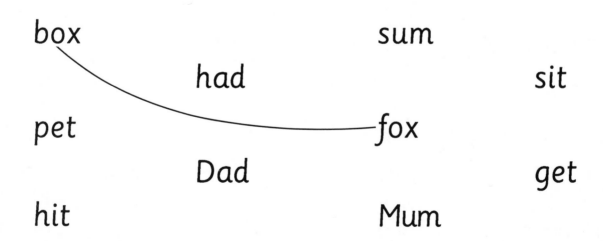

box   sum

had   sit

pet   fox

Dad   get

hit   Mum

FOLENS SPELLING - Basic Rules Book 1   F3892   © Folens.

Name _____   Date _____

The alphabet

a b c d e f g h i j k l m
n o p q r s t u v w x y z

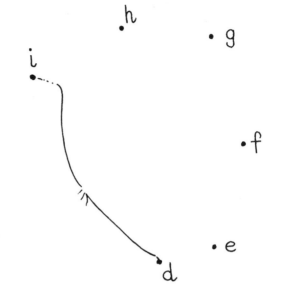

Join the dots in order, from a-z, to make the picture.

Write the alphabet.

a ... _____

_____

_____

How many letters are in the alphabet? _____

Alphabetical order

Put the words in alphabetical order.
Write the words next to the right letter.
The first one is done for you.

bed   van   cat   leg   egg

sun   pig   wig   you   on

dog   man   nut   ~~ant~~   gate

kite   up   jug   top   frog

x-ray   zoo   queen   ink   red   hat

a	ant	j		s	
b		k		t	
c		l		u	
d		m		v	
e		n		w	
f		o		x	
g		p		y	
h		q		z	
i		r			

Now write the alphabet.

a _____

_____

_____

Transport words

Here are some useful transport words.

car

motorbike

van

helicopter

lorry

ship

rocket

bus

bicycle

train

boat

aeroplane

Put the right words under the right picture.

Look at the   shape   of the word.

One is done for you.

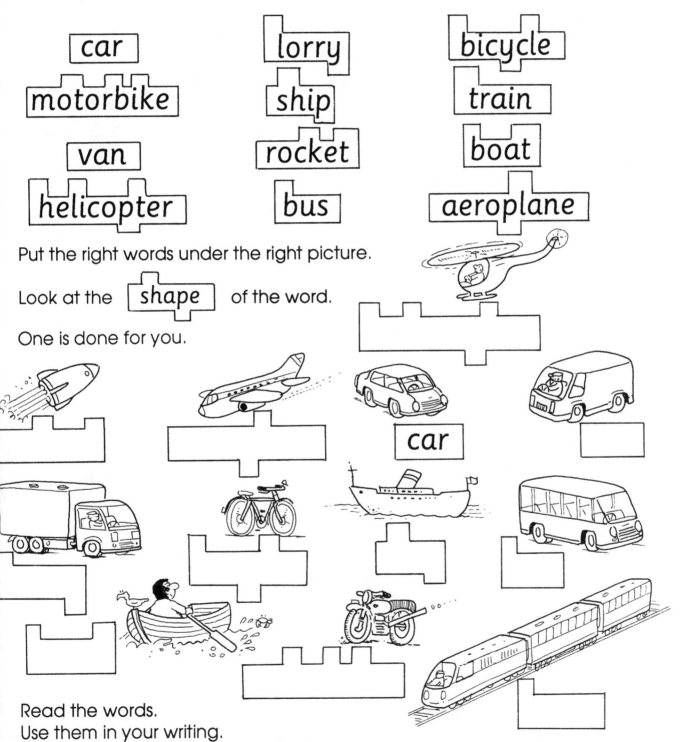

car

Read the words.
Use them in your writing.

Name _____   Date _____

Blends 1

Sometimes 2 consonants go together.
You can still hear the 2 sounds.
Say the sounds to yourself.

dr

br

cr

gr

pr

tr

Put in the right blends.

_ _ ass   _ _ idge   _ _ esent

gr
pr
fr
br
cr
tr
dr

_ _ iangle   _ _ oss   _ _ agon   _ _ uit

Look for these blends:

br   cr   dr

fr   gr   pr   tr

Colour them in to find
what is in the picture.

	cl		fl
bl		tw	
	gr	pr	
gl	br	dr	tr
			st
pl	cr	fr	tr
sl	sn	sc	sk

FOLENS SPELLING - Basic Rules Book 1 F3892   © Folens.

Blends 2

fl

Sometimes 2 consonants go together.
You can still hear the 2 sounds.
Say the sounds to yourself.

cl

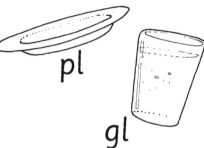

pl

bl

sl

gl

Put in the right blends.

_ _owers

_ _oud

_ _eep

gl
fl
pl
cl
bl
sl

_ _ay

_ _ack

_ _ue

Look for these blends:

bl   cl   fl
gl   pl   sl

Colour them in to find
what is in the picture.

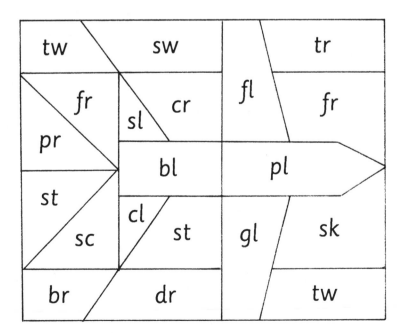

Blends 3

Sometimes 2 consonants go together.
You can still hear the 2 sounds.
Say the sounds to yourself.

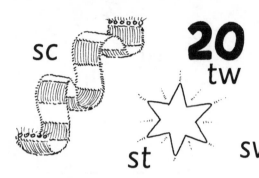

sc

20
tw

st

sk

sw

dw

sp

Put in the right blends.

_ _amp

_ _ail

_ _ider

12

_ _elve

_ _im

_ _ates

sp
sn
st
sk
tw
sw

Look for these blends:

st   sw   sc   sn
sp   sk   tw   dw

Colour them in to find
what is in the picture.

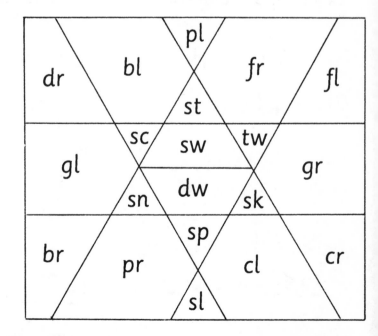

Name _____ Date _____

Colours

Learn to spell like this.

Look	Say	Cover	Write	Check

Write the words. Colour the boxes.

red _____ ☐   yellow _____ ☐
blue _____ ☐   green _____ ☐
black _____ ☐   white _____ ☐
orange _____ ☐   pink _____ ☐
brown _____ ☐   grey _____ ☐
purple _____ ☐   gold _____ ☐

Put in the missing words.
Colour the pictures.

The sky is _____

The grass is _____

My hair is _____

Tomatoes are _____

Bananas are _____

My eyes are _____

This page is _____

A £1 coin is _____

Name _____   Date _____

Wordsearch 2

Learn to spell like this.

Look	Say	Cover	Write	Check

Spell these words:

she _____   get _____

not _____   went _____

old _____   them _____

see _____   have _____

him _____   all _____

Now find the words in the wordsearch.
All the words go across. —➤ The first one is done for you.

a	s	e	e	b	w	e	n	t
s	s	h	e	c	e	i	n	f
c	b	a	l	l	a	s	t	b
g	a	t	f	t	h	e	m	i
n	o	t	e	t	s	i	a	e
a	e	s	h	a	v	e	i	o
o	l	d	s	o	u	t	e	b
i	g	e	t	b	h	i	m	t

Read these words: *see*   old   get   went
Use each word in a sentence.

1. _____

2. _____

3. _____

4. _____

FOLENS SPELLING - Basic Rules Book 1 F3892   © Folens.

Parts of the body

Put the names in the right places.

leg	foot	eyes	nose	hand
body	arm	head	ear	mouth

Now try to spell the words without looking.

_____   _____   _____   _____

_____   _____   _____   _____

oo and ee

A ghost goes **oo**.

A bat goes **ee**.

Put the **oo** words in the ghost.
Put the **ee** words in the bat.
The first one is done for you.

food
soon
look
cook
need
good
feed
cook
weed
wood
roof
moon
deep
room
been
feet
keep

Now put a word in place of each picture. Write the sentence.

👀 --- at the 🌙

_____ __ ___ ____

The 🐝 is on the 🏠

___ __ __ __ ___

I have 👢 on my 🦶

___ ___ __ __ ___

look

bee

moon

boots

feet

roof

Name _____   Date _____

Animal names

There are the names of **10 pets** here.
Find them and put the words on the lines underneath.
The first one is done for you.

cat|dog mouse rabbit hamster budgie fish rat parrot turtle

cat _____   _____   _____   _____   _____

_____   _____   _____   _____   _____

There are the names of **10 wild animals** here.
Find them and put the words on the lines underneath.
The first one is done for you.

snake|elephant tiger lion giraffe monkey deer hippo panda zebra

snake _____   _____   _____   _____

_____   _____   _____   _____   _____

Read the words.
Turn over and make a different name list for a friend to do.

Name _____   Date _____

Spell **sh** words

s and **h** go together to make a quiet sound. **sh!**

Sh! The sheep are
sleeping.

Write the correct words under the pictures.

ship	shed	sheep	shell	shop	shoe

_____   _____   _____

   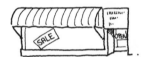

_____   _____   _____

Read the words and use each word in a sentence.

1. _____

2. _____

3. _____

4. _____

5. _____

6. _____

Here are some more **sh** words.
Spell them. Read the words.

she ————   should ————   shut ————

push ————   wish ————   fish ————

FOLENS SPELLING - Basic Rules Book 1 F3892   © Folens.

Name _____ Date _____

Spooky words

werewolf

bats

castle

cold

ghost

haunted

monster   creepy   vampire   rats

howl

cry

moon

old   owl

scare

scream

witch

Use some of these words to write a spooky story, or poem.

Name _____   Date _____

Days of the week

There are 7 days in the week.
Spell them - you can see they all end in **day**.

Write each one **twice**. Read them.

Monday   _____   _____

Tuesday   _____   _____

Wednesday   _____   _____

Thursday   _____   _____

Friday   _____   _____

Saturday   _____   _____

Sunday   _____   _____

Put in the missing words.

My best day is _____.

The 2 days of the weekend are _____ and _____.

We come back to school on _____.

Now answer these questions:

Which day is named after the sun? _____

Which day is named after the moon? _____

Which day has 9 letters in it? _____

Which day is it today? _____

FOLENS SPELLING - Basic Rules Book 1 F3892   © Folens.

Spell ch words

c and h go together to make a loud sound. **ch!**

I like chops and chips.

Write the correct words under the pictures.

| chips | chain | chimney | chicken | chair | cherries |

_____   _____   _____

_____   _____   _____

Read the words and use each word in a sentence.

1. _____

2. _____

3. _____

4. _____

5. _____

6. _____

Here are some more **ch** words. Spell them. Read the words.

child _____   children _____   chin _____

rich _____   such _____   much _____

Months of the year

There are 12 months in the year.
Learn to spell like this:

Look	Say	Cover	Write	Check

January _____   July   _____

February _____   August   _____

March _____   September   _____

April _____   October   _____

May _____   November   _____

June _____   December   _____

Now answer these questions:

1. Which months end in y? _____

2. Which month is it now? _____

3. Which month has your birthday in it? _____

Do you know the 4 seasons?

spring	summer	autumn	winter

Spell them:

_____   _____

_____   _____

FOLENS SPELLING - Basic Rules Book 1 F3892   © Folens.

Spell **th** words

t and **h** go together to make one sound. **th**!

` Thank you for the bag.´

Write the correct words under the pictures.

three	thumb	thorn	throne

Here are some more **th** words.
Spell them:

the _____   then _____   them _____

there _____   this _____   that _____

Read the words.
Use each word in a sentence.

1. _____

2. _____

3. _____

4. _____

5. _____

6. _____

Food words

Write the words underneath.

spaghetti   bread

meat

milk

fish   coffee

crisps   samosas

tomatoes   sausages

pizza   burger   tea   sugar   apples

cheese   coke   bananas   cake

Read the words.

What do **you** like to eat?
Make a list of the things
you like. (You can put
other things too.)

shopping list

Now **you** can write the shopping list at home!

Name _____ Date _____

Numbers

Learn to spell like this:

Look	Say	Cover	Write	Check

Spell these words: 0 zero

- one _____   :::six _____
- •• two _____   ::::seven _____
- ••• three _____   ::::eight _____
- :: four _____   :::::nine _____
- ::• five _____   ::::::ten _____

I have ....   Put in the right **word**.

I have _____ head
I have _____ trees
I have _____ toes
I have _____ flags
I have _____ pens
I have _____ hands
I have _____ cats
I have _____ books
I have _____ ships
I have _____ fingers

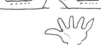

Put in the right **word**.

one + two = _____   ten - one = _____
seven + three = _____   six - three = _____
two + five = _____   eight - two = _____
one + one = _____   seven - two = _____

FOLENS SPELLING - Basic Rules Book 1 F3892

Name _____   Date _____

Rhyme time 2

Some words rhyme.

cat and **hat**

Read these rhyming words:

man	van
pig	wig
dog	fog
bug	mug
hen	pen

Put the right sentence by the right picture.

A hen is in a pen

_____

A bug is in a mug

_____

A man is in a van

_____

A pig is in a wig

_____

A dog is in the fog

_____

Little words in BIG words

Look for little words in a big word.
Put a ring round the little words like this.

(is)(and)

is   and

candle

grandmother

together

Saturday

sunshine

interesting   Canada

forgotten   dragon

Did you find these words? Spell them.

is _____	and _____	for _____	to _____
ten _____	on _____	the _____	day _____
in _____	can _____	get _____	sun _____

Find 4 little words in this big word. **transformation**

Write 2 big words which have little words in them.

_____   _____

Name _____   Date _____

Count the vowels

a e i o u are vowels.

Every word has to have one vowel or more.

w**i**tch
has one
vowel in it.

t**e**l**e**v**i**s**io**n
has five
vowels in it.

Write your name _____

How many vowels in your name? _____

Put a ring round each vowel in these words.
The first one is done for you.

h(o)l(i)d(a)y   going   apple   house   car

children   Saturday   window   today   supermarket

elephant   look

Look at the words and count the vowels.

Which word has 1 vowel in it? _____

Which word has 2 vowels in it? _____

Which word has 3 vowels in it? _____

Which word has 4 vowels in it? _____

Look at this word: *facetious*

Find the vowels. Write them _____

How many vowels in this word? _____

supercalifragilisticexpialidocious

(Mary Poppins 1964)

Name _____   Date _____

Syllables

A syllable is a group of letters.
A syllable can be one little word or part of a bigger word.

mouse   = 1 syllable

rab/bit   = 2 syllables

el/e/phant   = 3 syllables

Every syllable must have a vowel in it - or more than one vowel.
The vowels are **a e i o u.**

Put a line through these words to show where the syllables are.
The first one is done for you.

 snow/man

 lighthouse

 telephone

 butterfly

 teapot

 bookcase

Now do the same with these words.

Sunday	window	pencil
dragon	yesterday	holiday
telephone	umbrella	postbox

Word sums

Learn to spell like this.

Look	Say	Cover	Write	Check

Make one big word from 2 little words.

up + set	=	<u>upset</u> _____
down + hill	=	_____
some + one	=	_____
car + pet	=	_____
book + case	=	_____
snow + man	=	_____
post + man	=	_____
up + on	=	_____
to + day	=	_____

Now can you make 2 little words from each big word?
Write the little words underneath.

into	sunshine	forget	Sunday
___ ___	___ ___	___ ___	___ ___
uphill	postcard	sunset	seaside
___ ___	___ ___	___ ___	___ ___

Name _____   Date _____

 # Magic 'e'

Magic **'e'** (sometimes called lazy **'e'** or silent **'e'**) makes the vowel before the **e** say its name.

Say these words:

hat   **hate**   bit   **bite**   not   **note**   tub   **tube**

<u>hate</u>

<u>bite</u>

<u>note</u>

<u>tube</u>

Add **'e'** to the end of these words.
Write the new words.
Read them.

hat	→ _____		bit	→ _____
mat	→ _____		win	→ _____
Sam	→ _____		rid	→ _____
can	→ _____		pip	→ _____
not	→ _____		tub	→ _____
hop	→ _____		cub	→ _____
rod	→ _____		cut	→ _____
mop	→ _____		us	→ _____

Now put these 4 words into 4 sentences.

same   _____

ride   _____

hope   _____

cube   _____

Wordsearch 3

Learn to spell like this:

Look	Say	Cover	Write	Check

Spell these words:

put _____	said _____	back _____
one _____	with _____	little _____
they _____	make _____	there _____
and _____	when _____	about _____
you _____	give _____	right _____
was _____	down _____	other _____

Now find the words in the wordsearch.
All the words go across. ⟶   The first one is done for you.

a	o	t	h	e	r	e	a	b	a	n	d
j	k	o	n	e	s	g	i	v	e	r	t
s	a	i	d	h	g	t	p	b	a	c	k
i	y	o	u	f	l	i	t	t	l	e	d
d	o	w	n	a	b	e	p	u	t	a	b
l	r	i	g	h	t	o	a	w	i	t	h
b	m	n	t	h	e	c	z	h	i	j	e
a	m	a	k	e	y	g	a	b	o	u	t
w	a	s	u	v	w	h	e	n	l	m	e
b	c	p	w	t	h	e	y	d	e	f	t

Turn over and make a wordsearch for your friend.
1. Make a list of 10 words to find.
2. Make a grid 10 cm x 10 cm.
3. Write one word on each line.
4. Fill up the empty squares with other letters.

FOLENS SPELLING - Basic Rules Book 1 F3892   © Folens.

Name _____   Date _____

Question words

There are 7 useful question words.
Learn to spell them.

when   _____

where   _____

which   _____

what   _____

why   _____

who   _____

how   _____

Read the words.
Now answer these questions in sentences.

1. When do you go to bed?

_____

2. Where do you live?

_____

3. Which day is it?

_____

4. What is your name?

_____

5. Why do we eat?

_____

6. Who is your friend?

_____

7. How do you get to school?

_____

Now turn over and write a sentence using each question word.

Adding **ing**

Go!

I am going.

Add **ing** to these words. Write the new words.

play   _playing_   fish   _____

wish   _____   look   _____

cook   _____   kick   _____

jump   _____   miss   _____

Use 2 of these **ing** words in sentences.

1. _____

2. _____

After a single vowel and a single consonant double the last letter and add **ing**.

shop   _shopping_   hug   _____

swim   _____   rob   _____

win   _____   skip   _____

clap   _____   beg   _____

Use 2 of these **ing** words in sentences.

1. _____

2. _____

When a word ends in magic **'e'**, drop the **'e'** and add **ing**. Spell these words.

like   _liking_   take   _____

hope   _____   ride   _____

love   _____   make   _____

Adding ed

Add **ed** to these words.
It sounds like **'d'** or **'t'**
Write the new words.

look <u>looked</u>   pull _____

fish _____   milk _____

jump _____   cook _____

kick _____   fill _____

Use 2 of these **ed** words in sentences.

1. _____

2. _____

After a single vowel and a single consonant double the last letter and add **ed**.

shop <u>shopped</u>   skip _____

beg _____   hug _____

trip _____   clap _____

rub _____   chop _____

Use 2 of these **ed** words in sentences.

1. _____

2. _____

When a word ends in magic **'e'**, just add the **'d'**. Spell these words.

hope <u>hoped</u>   live _____

like _____   hate _____

save _____   love _____

Read the words.

Rhyme time 3

Some words rhyme.

all - ball - call - fall - hall - tall - wall

This sentence has rhyming words in it:-

A **dog** went for a j**og**
and saw a **frog** on
a **log** in the **fog**.

Now put a line under the words which rhyme in these sentences.

1. A fat cat sat on a mat with a bat in his hat.

2. A pig in a wig ate a fig with a twig.

3. Jack had a sack and a back-pack.

4. The fish made a wish on the dish.

5. Ten men and Ben put the hen in a pen.

Make up sentences with these rhyming words in them.

| took | look | book |

1. _____

| king | swing | ring |

2. _____

| make | cake | take |

3. _____

Name _____   Date _____

Spellings to take home

Parents

Please can you help your child learn these 5 spellings for next

Monday ☐
Tuesday ☐
Wednesday ☐
Thursday ☐
Friday ☐

(Tick the box.)

Don't let them copy the word letter by letter.

Do help them this way:

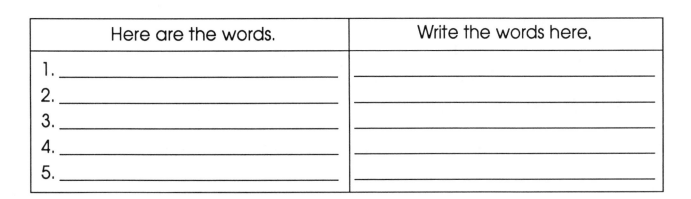

Look at the word

Say the word

Cover the word

Write the word

Check the word

Here are the words.	Write the words here.
1. _____	_____
2. _____	_____
3. _____	_____
4. _____	_____
5. _____	_____

Were the words   too easy? ☐
too hard? ☐
about right? ☐

(Tick the box.)

Please send the sheet back to school. Thank you for helping.

Name _____   Date _____

Improve your spelling!

Answer these questions by putting a ring round or .

I say words clearly.	yes	no
I look at words carefully.	yes	no
I listen carefully.	yes	no
I write neatly.	yes	no
I use a word book or dictionary.	yes	no
I have a go at a spelling.	yes	no
I learn spellings each week.	yes	no

Read these sentences and think about what **YOU** could do to improve your spelling.

I am going to say words more clearly.
I am going to look at words more carefully.
I am going to listen more carefully.
I am going to write more neatly.
I am going to use a word book or a dictionary.
I am going to have a go at a spelling.
I am going to learn spellings each week.

Write here what **you** are going to do to improve your spelling.

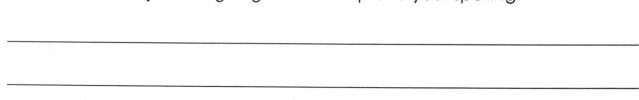

_____

_____

Signed: _____   Date: _____

FOLENS SPELLING - Basic Rules Book 1 F3892   © Folens.

Word list 1

Regular monosyllabic words with short vowels.

a	rag	fit	dog	hum
at	sag	hit	fog	Mum
bat	tag	lit	hog	rum
cat	wag	pit	jog	sum
fat		sit	log	yum
mat	**e**	wit	dot	us
pat	Ben	bid	got	bus
rat	den	did	hot	bun
sat	hen	hid	jot	fun
vat	men	kid	lot	pun
an	pen	lid	not	run
ban	ten	dim	pot	sun
can	bet	him	rot	bud
Dan	get	rim	tot	cud
fan	jet	Tim	on	mud
man	let	is	Ron	but
pan	met	his	box	cut
ran	net	in	fox	gut
tan	pet	bin	pox	hut
am	set	din	cod	jut
ham	vet	fin	God	nut
jam	wet	kin	nod	rut
Pam	yet	pin	pod	bug
Sam	bed	sin	rod	dug
cap	led	tin	Bob	hug
map	fed	win	job	jug
tap	Ned	dip	mob	mug
bad	red	hip	sob	rug
Dad	Ted	lip		tug
had	wed	nip	**u**	
lad	beg	pip	up	
mad	leg	rip	cup	
pad	Meg	sip	pup	
sad	peg	tip	sup	
as	yes	zip	cub	
bag			hub	
gag	**i**	**o**	rub	
lag	it	bog	tub	
nag	bit	cog	gum	

Word list 2

Words with blends and double letters

brick	stick	sock
brown	swing	all
brush	swim	ball
bring	scarf	call
drum	spot	fall
dress	spell	hall
drop	smack	small
frog	smell	tall
free	snap	wall
from	snip	see
grip	skull	seen
grin	skip	seed
green	shot	feel
Gran	sheep	feet
crab	shop	feed
cross	fish	bee
pram	wish	been
press	dish	need
trip	chop	weed
tree	chip	keep
black	chin	deep
blue	much	week
bless	such	Queen
clock	thin	too
clap	thick	roof
flag	this	room
flat	that	food
flop	with	boot
glad	them	pool
glue	which	moon
glass	wheel	soon
play	back	book
plan	duck	cook
plum	Jack	took
slip	kick	look
slide	lick	hook
slap	lock	good
twig	neck	wood
twin	peck	hood
stop	rock	spoon

FOLENS SPELLING - Basic Rules Book 1 F3892

Word list 3

100 most used words in English.

a	did	is	on	they
about	do	it	one	this
all	down	just	only	to
an	first	like	or	two
and	for	little	our	up
are	from	look	over	want
as	get	made	other	was
at	got	make	out	we
back	had	me	right	well
be	has	more	said	went
been	have	much	see	were
before	he	must	she	what
big	her	my	so	when
but	here	new	some	where
by	him	no	that	which
call	his	not	the	who
came	I	now	their	will
can	if	of	them	with
come	in	off	then	you
could	into	old	there	your

Other useful words.

after	ask	fast	money	please
again	because	friend	mother	pull
along	brother	give	nothing	put
animal	children	going	once	should
another	dinner	happy	open	talk
around	every	morning	people	walk

* **Source**: - J. McNally and W. Murray, 'Key words to Literacy'. (See Appendix)

* **Source**: - National Curriculum documents; 'Attack' spelling programme. (See Appendix)

APPENDIX

Books

1. Bissex, G.L. (1980) *Gnys at Wrk*. Harvard University Press.
2. Bryant, P.E. and Bradley, L. (1985) *Children's Reading Problems*. Blackwell.
3. Daniels, J.C. and Diack, H. (1979) *The Standard Reading Tests*. Hart-Davis
4. Gentry, J.R. (1987) *Spel..... is a Four Letter Word*. Scholastic.
5. Hornsby, B. and Shear, F. (1976) *Alpha to Omega*. Heinemann.
6. McNally, B. and Murray, W. (1970) *Key Words to Literacy*. The Teacher Publishing Company, Northants.
7. National Curriculum Documents, (1989) *English in the National Curriculum,*. H.M.S.O.
8. Peters, M.L. (1975) *Diagnostic and Remedial Spelling Manual*. Macmillan.
9. Schonell, F.J. (1976) *Graded Word Spelling Test*. L.D.A.
10. Torbe, M. (1977) *Teaching Spelling*. Ward Lock Educational.
11. Vernon, P.E. (1977) *Spelling Test*. N.F.E.R.
12. Vincent, D. and Claydon, J. (1982) *Diagnostic Spelling Test*. N.F.E.R. Nelson.

Programmes/workbooks

1. *Attack Spelling Programme*.
   100 systematically structured spelling lessons. (1980) Richards, J.P.B.S. Nottingham.
2. *Catchwords - Ideas for Teaching Spelling*.
   A set of six graded workbooks. (1978) Cripps, C. Harcourt, Brace, Jovanovich.
3. Dictionaries - *A.C.E.* (Aurally Coded English) L.D.A.
   Pergamon Dictionary of Perfect Spelling. Pergamon.
   Both these dictionaries are for children who experience difficulties with spelling. Words can be found according to their sound - e.g., psychology can be found under 'p' and 's'.
4. *Spelling Made Easy*. Brand, V., Egon Publishers Ltd.
5. *Sounds, Pictures, Words*. Graded workbooks for 5-8 year olds. Hughes, J. Nelson.
6. *Stile Spelling Programme*. Self-correcting spelling programme for 5-14 year olds. L.D.A.

Spellchecker

Franklin Elementary Spellmaster .(QES90) (Designed for children - 26,800 words in it.) Innovations International Ltd., Richmond, Surrey.

Computer programs

Animated Alphabet. Sherston Software, Malmesbury, Wiltshire.
Hands on Spelling. E.S.M. Cambs. (Training visual memory.)
Star Spell. Fisher Marriott, Lower Fulbrook, Warwick, CV35 8AS.